HIGH-FREQUENCY
WORDS

AGES 4 TO 5

SUE GRAVES

© 2003 Scholastic Ltd
Text © Sue Graves 2003

Author
Sue Graves

Editor
Roanne Davis

Assistant Editor
Dulcie Booth

Designer
Heather Sanneh

Illustrations
Mary Hall

Cover illustration
Claire Crystall

Published by Scholastic Ltd,
Villiers House,
Clarendon Avenue,
Leamington Spa,
Warwickshire CV32 5PR

Printed by Bell & Bain Ltd, Glasgow

5 6 7 8 9 0   5 6 7 8 9 0 1 2

British Library Cataloguing-in-Publication Data
A catalogue record for this book is available from the British Library.

ISBN 0-439-98334-7

CONTENTS

INTRODUCTION

HIGH-FREQUENCY WORDS

High-frequency words are those words that every child needs in order to read even the most simple texts. The National Literacy Strategy emphasises the importance of these words in 'holding together the general coherence of texts', and stresses that 'early familiarity with them will help pupils get pace and accuracy into their reading at an early stage.' Teachers often find that children can sight-read fairly difficult words such as *clown* and *elephant* quite early in the process of learning to read, mainly because of the word's unusual shape or sound. However, many children find it hard to recall high-frequency words, especially those with difficult or irregular spelling patterns such as *said*, *come* and *was*. High-frequency words, set apart from other vocabulary, elicit little meaning and therefore recalling them 'on sight' can prove difficult for many children. It is with this in mind that this series of minibooks has been created.

ABOUT THIS BOOK

This book contains a series of photocopiable minibooks that gradually introduce the high-frequency words listed in the National Literacy Strategy for Reception year. The words are introduced in banks of between three and six, in set patterns, to encourage both successful prediction and sufficient practice of the words. The minibooks provide the children with the experience of making their own reading books and the development of the skills that this task involves, such as sequencing pages; identifying front and back covers, illustrations and so on. The design of the books also allows the children to colour the drawings as they wish.

As well as the photocopiable minibooks, this book contains:
● an overview grid including the high-frequency words covered in each minibook
● teaching ideas and differentiated activities linked to the minibooks and to the National Literacy Strategy objectives
● photocopiable activity sheets for group or individual work
● homework or extension sheets
● flashcards
● record charts to assess the reading and spelling attainment of all the high-frequency words addressed in the minibooks.

ACTIVITIES

Each minibook has linked photocopiable sheets to provide reinforcement work of the high-frequency words in the reading book, whether they are being introduced for the first time or not.

The two activity sheets are included according to difficulty; the first having easier tasks than the second. You may wish to let the children try both, or use them purely to differentiate the work in group time.

The third sheet is designed as a homework exercise, and/or for extension work during the lesson. Each one requires few resources other than a pencil or crayons in order to complete it, and the help of a parent or carer. You will need to decide whether the homework task is appropriate for all the children in the class or group.

LEARNING AND PRACTISING HIGH-FREQUENCY WORDS

As the main thrust of these minibooks is the learning and reinforcement of high-frequency words, it may be helpful at this point to identify useful activities that should help to speed up this process.

At the back of this resource book are photocopiable flashcards. You may prefer to use them purely as flashcards during whole class teaching sessions, or during group work to practise sight recognition of words prior to reading the books. However, the following activities all give extra practice for learning new words and reinforcing those already introduced:

● Play a 'Snap'-type game, using two copies of each card. Spread the cards face-up on the table and invite the children, in turn, to find matching pairs. If the child has correctly matched a pair on sight, he or she keeps the pair. If not, the cards are returned to the table for another child to have a turn. Continue until all the pairs have been collected. If wished, count up the pairs to find a winner.

● Give the children a set of flashcards each, with the words cut into individual letters. Place a set of whole-word cards in the middle of the table. In turn, ask each child to choose a word and read it aloud to the others. The child then turns the card face down so that no one can see it. Everyone then has to make the word by picking out the individual letters before him or her.

Continue until all the words have been read and spelled. Encourage the children to proof-read their own and each other's words. Where a word has been spelled incorrectly, invite the children to suggest corrections.

● If wished, the flashcards can be enlarged to make a target-word display in the classroom. This gives you the opportunity to encourage the children to read the words and use them in independent writing activities.

HOW TO USE THE MINIBOOKS
MAKING THE BOOKS

Initially, you will need to demonstrate to the children how the books are put together. Indeed, you may find it preferable in the early stages to prepare the books before the lesson. Gradually, though, the children should be encouraged to make their own books.

1. Photocopy the book pages onto A4 paper, or A3 for whole class or larger group teaching.

2. Fold the front and back cover sheet in half. Keep the fold line to the left-hand side.

3. Fold the inner pages in half. Keep the fold line of these pages on the right.

4. Place the inner pages inside the cover.

5. Either staple along the spine or open the book up and sew along the spine.

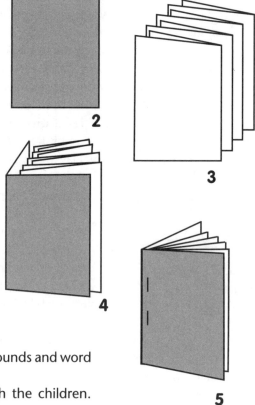

USING THE MINIBOOKS

Introduce the new high-frequency words covered in each minibook, using the photocopiable flashcards. Encourage the children to recognise the words on sight. During the learning process, draw attention to initial and final sounds and word shape and length.

Go through the minibook with the children. Encourage them to predict any new words on the page by looking carefully for picture clues, start sounds and so on.

Use the minibooks as starting points for discussion, encouraging the children to draw on their own experiences of topics and situations developed in each book.

Encourage the children to colour the pictures carefully. Remind them that this is their own special book that they are making and to take pride in its appearance.

Record each child's reading and spelling attainment by completing the charts on pages 56 and 57 of this book.

It is suggested that the minibook is read first and that the activities linked to the book are treated as follow-up and reinforcement exercises. The activities provide useful opportunities to revisit the stories and work on reading and spelling patterns addressed by them. Following discussion, the children should be encouraged to work independently on the photocopiable sheets. Go through the completed work with the children to check for understanding, and provide further practice where necessary, using resources and ideas suggested earlier in this introduction.

After the first six books and activities, you might want to give a short reading and spelling test as suggested by the record charts on pages 56 and 57. The scores can help to create a profile of each child's literacy attainment.

Overview grid

Title	Page	High-frequency words (new)	High-frequency words (revised)	Activity pages	NLS objectives covered in activities
I am a boy...	58	I, am, a		9–11	W2, S4, T1
The third little pig	63	look, at, me, and		13–15	W9, W4, S3, T1
Poor Cinderella	68	all, day	I	17–19	W7, S1, T11
Playtime	73	he, can, play, the, on, she	a, me	21–3	W2, S2, T11
Let's fly	78	my, mum, dad, said, no, yes	I, and	25–7	W2, S1, T2
Mum's birthday	83	they, are, going, to, get	mum	29–31	W5, W9, S3, T1, T12
This is the dog...	88	dog, was, in, cat	the	33–5	W9, S3, T7
Sunita's search	93	went, up	to, she, the	37–9	W2, S3, T1
Who goes there?	98	you, see, this, big	can	41–3	W2, S1, T11
A party	103	we, like, of	all	45–7	W5, S3, T14
Coming and going	108	go, away, come		49–51	W7, S2, T12
Surprise parcel	113	is, it, for	you, no, mum, me, yes, the, dog	53–5	W9, S4, T12

TEACHER'S NOTES

I am a boy...

HIGH-FREQUENCY WORDS: *I, AM, A*

I am a boy...

WHOLE CLASS TEACHING

Practise the high-frequency words *I, am* and *a*, using the flashcards. Remind the children that the word *I* is always written with a capital letter. Ask them if they can think of other words that always begin with capital letters. (Their own names, for example.)

Read the minibook together. As you read, ask the children to predict unknown words by looking for picture clues and by paying particular attention to initial sounds.

Ask the children to track the text to find all the high-frequency words. See, for example, how many times they can find the word *am*.

After reading, talk about playing at dressing up. Encourage the children to tell you what they like to pretend to be when they are playing.

GROUP/INDIVIDUAL WORK

Go through the minibook again, pointing out that each sentence tells us what is happening in the picture. Then, according to ability, give each child one of the photocopiable sheets.

I AM..., page 9

Ask the children to draw pictures of themselves on the sheet, then trace the words and complete the sentence by writing their name in the space. They should then write out the whole sentence underneath. (Remind the children to start their names with a capital letter.)

DRESSING UP, page 10

Ask the children to look carefully at the pictures on the sheet and then choose the correct sentence from the side of the page to fit each picture. Let them colour the pictures when they have finished.

PLENARY

Revisit the high-frequency words with the children. Check that they can read them on sight.

Show some of the children's work to the others. Did they remember to write their names with an initial capital letter ('I am...')? Check that they wrote the correct sentence for each picture on 'Dressing up'.

You could help the children make a wall display of some of the people they like to pretend to be when they are dressing up and playing.

EXTENSION

WHAT ANIMAL AM I?, page 11

In this activity, the children can practise the words they have been learning in a different context.

I am...

● Draw a picture of yourself.

● Trace the words. Then finish the sentence by writing your name.

I am _____

● Now write the whole sentence again.

_____

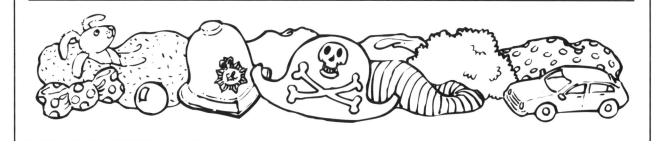

Dressing up

● Look at the pictures and read the sentences. Write the correct sentence under each picture.

I am a king.

I am a clown.

I am a pirate.

I am a lion.

What animal am I?

- ● Complete the sentences. (One has been done for you.)
- ● Then colour the pictures.

I am a hen.

_____
cat.

_____
dog.

_____
mouse.

The third little pig

OBJECTIVES

Word level: to recognise the critical features of words, for example their shape; to discriminate onsets from rimes in speech and spelling.

Sentence level: to understand that words are ordered left to right and need to be read that way to make sense.

Text level: to track the text in the right order, page by page, left to right.

WHOLE CLASS TEACHING

Practise the high-frequency words using flashcards, prior to reading the minibook. In particular, point out the shape of the words. On a board or flip chart, draw the outline shapes of the words and ask the children to identify which word would fit into which shape.

Read the minibook together. Remind the children to read the text across from left to right and to turn the pages over one at a time.

Ask the children if they know the traditional story of the Three Little Pigs. Encourage them to retell the story to the rest of the group.

Re-read pages 5 and 6 of the minibook. Ask the children to identify the rhyming words on these pages (*huffing* and *puffing).* Point out that a different word has been created from *huffing* by changing the initial letter, to make *puffing.* Develop the idea of creating rhyming words in this way by writing the word *at* on the board. Ask the children to help you create a rhyming word string by changing initial letters, for example *cat, bat, rat, mat, sat* and so on. Encourage the children to identify the onset and the rime in each word.

GROUP/INDIVIDUAL WORK

LOOK AT ME!, page 13

Ask the children to write the words *Look at me* in the characters' speech bubbles on the sheet. Remind them to proof-read their spellings when they have finished.

THE LITTLE PIG'S HOUSE, page 14

Show the photocopiable sheet to the children. Ask them to read the words on the little pig's house and colour each section according to the colour code.

PLENARY

Select children from each activity task to share their work. Check that the spellings on the first sheet are correct and that each word box on the second has been coloured correctly. Using photocopiable page 14, let the children see how fast they can read each word aloud.

EXTENSION

WHAT I LIKE DOING, page 15

As an extension or for homework, ask the children to think about something they like doing and to complete the photocopiable sheet. Remind the children of the *-ing* words they read in the minibook and re-read them together.

Look at me!

● Write **Look at me** in each speech bubble.

waving!

running!

huffing!

hiding!

laughing!

puffing!

The little pig's house

● Colour:

look – red	**at** – yellow	**me** – green

What I like doing

● Draw a picture of yourself doing something that you enjoy.

● Write about the picture by completing the sentence with a word ending in **ing**:

Look at me _____

● Now write the whole sentence again.

_____

Poor Cinderella

HIGH-FREQUENCY WORDS: *ALL, DAY, (I)*

WHOLE CLASS TEACHING

Before reading the minibook, practise the new high-frequency words using the flashcards. Ask the children if they know the story of Cinderella. Encourage them to talk about the story.

Read the book together and help the children to decode unfamiliar words by looking at picture clues.

Ask the children to choose one of the activities shown in the book, for example *I wash all day*, and write this sentence on a board or flip chart. Point out that it doesn't matter if the sentence is written on the board, or printed in the book – if the sentence is the same, the meaning remains the same.

Cover the text on page 3 and show the children the picture only. Ask if the sentence on the board (*I wash all day*) makes sense for this picture. Ask the children to suggest what the sentence should say. Uncover the text on the page to allow the children to see if they were right.

GROUP/INDIVIDUAL WORK

MATCH UP, page 17

Ask the children to look at the pictures and read the sentences, then link each picture to its right sentence. Remind them to look at clues in the pictures to help them. If necessary, let the children refer to the book to help them complete this activity.

ALL DAY, page 18

Show the children the photocopiable sheet and explain that they should complete sentences from the story that have words missing. They should then copy each sentence carefully on the lines provided.

PLENARY

Ask a group of children from each activity task to show their work to the others. Tell the children who completed 'Match up' to check that they have matched the pictures and sentences correctly. Ask the children who worked on 'All day' to read out their sentences.

As a whole class exercise, revisit the high-frequency words for this minibook and check that the children can read them on sight. Similarly, make flashcards of less familiar words, for example *sweep* and *shout*, and encourage the children to read these on sight too.

EXTENSION

SORTING WORDS, page 19

To reinforce recognition of these words, ask the children to cut out and paste the words into the correct boxes on the photocopiable sheet.

Match up

● Match each picture to the right sentence.

I shout all day.

I sleep all day.

I cook all day.

I wash all day.

All day

● Add the missing words. Then write out the sentences.

I wash all day.

I sweep _____ _____.

_____ search _____ day.

I sleep _____ day.

SCHOLASTIC **PHOTOCOPIABLE**

Sorting words

● Read the words at the bottom of the page. Cut them out and stick them into the right boxes.

I	all	day

✂ -

I	day	all	day	all	I
day	day	all	I	I	all

Playtime

HIGH-FREQUENCY WORDS: *HE, CAN, PLAY, THE, ON, SHE, (A), (ME)*

OBJECTIVES

Word level: to read letters that represent the sounds *sh* and *th*.

Sentence level: to use awareness of the grammar of a sentence to predict words during shared reading and when re-reading familiar stories.

Text level: to understand that writing is formed directionally, a word at a time.

WHOLE CLASS TEACHING

Before reading the minibook, use the flashcards to practise the new high-frequency words. Draw particular attention to *he* and *she*. Demonstrate how the letters *s* and *h* together are said *sh*. Similarly, point out the digraph *th* in *the.* Encourage the children to think of words beginning with *sh* and *th*. Write their suggestions on a board or flip chart. Select volunteers to come to the board to circle the *sh* or *th* sound in the words listed.

Whilst reading the book together, encourage the children to predict unfamiliar words by considering the grammar of each sentence. To demonstrate this, re-read the first sentence and help the children to understand how it has been ordered (subject – verb – object – where the action takes place). Ask the children to look for this order on other pages. Similarly, encourage them to predict unfamiliar or more difficult words, such as *ice, roundabout, computer* by using picture clues.

Ask the children to find the page that has the sentence *She can play the drums on a bed.* Write the sentence on the board as the children dictate it to you. Demonstrate that the sentence has to be written across the board from left to right and one word at a time. Select children to identify the high-frequency words in the sentence.

GROUP/INDIVIDUAL WORK

FIND THE WORD, page 21

Read the instructions and first example on the sheet. Advise the children that they must look carefully at the word in bold in the box on the left and then track the rest of the corresponding list to find that word.

SCRAMBLE!, page 22

Tell the children to unscramble the letters in the TVs on the sheet to make words they know and write the correct word on the line provided. Emphasise that they are finding words from the minibook. Ask them to check that the words they make can be found in the book.

PLENARY

Invite children from each activity task to show their work to the others. Ask the children to read aloud the matching word in each line of text in 'Find the word'. Encourage the rest of the class to check for errors. Ask the children to check that the unscrambled words in 'Scramble!' have been spelled correctly and if not, to suggest corrections.

Using the flashcards, check that the children can read on sight all the new high-frequency words for this minibook.

EXTENSION

WHAT CAN SHE PLAY?, page 23

Explain to the children that they should reorder the sentence so that it makes sense. Remind them to look for the capital letter to indicate the start of the sentence and to locate the full stop to mark the end of it.

Find the word

● Read the word in bold. Find it in the list and circle it.
● Then write the word on the line.

can	car cap cup can came _____
he	her here he hen hem _____
play	plug plan ploy plays play _____
on	an or am on of _____
she	shy shoo she shed he _____

Scramble!

● Sort these letters to make words.
Write the words.

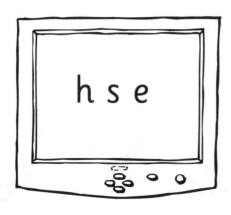

What can she play?

● Read these words and put them in order so that
the sentence makes sense.

can   She   play   ice.   on   hockey

_____

_____

Let's fly

OBJECTIVES

Word level: to identify and write initial and final phonemes in consonant–vowel–consonant (CVC) words.

Sentence level: to expect written text to make sense and to check for sense if it does not.

Text level: to use a variety of cues when reading: knowledge of the story and its context, and awareness of how it should make sense grammatically.

WHOLE CLASS TEACHING

Practise the new high-frequency words for this minibook using flashcards.

Read the minibook together. Talk about why the parent birds want the fledglings to leave the nest and compare this with the fledglings' reluctance. Explain that the parents are trying to get the birds to fly for their own good.

Discuss other occasions when a parent or carer may say *yes* or *no* to a child. Encourage the children to draw on their own experiences of when they have or have not been allowed to do something or have had to do something they were a bit scared of doing. Did they realise, later, that their parents said *yes* or *no* for their benefit?

Go through the book a second time, covering up the text on each page. Ask the children to decide from the picture clue whether the bird in the illustration is saying *yes* or *no*. Remind the children that picture clues like this can help them to decode unfamiliar words in texts.

Write the words *mum* and *dad* on a board or flip chart. Ask the children to identify the initial and final phonemes in these words.

GROUP/INDIVIDUAL WORK

YES OR NO, page 25

Tell the children to look at each picture carefully and decide whether the bird is saying *yes* or *no*. They should write the appropriate word in the speech bubble and use it to complete the sentence underneath. Then ask them to write the sentence again on the line provided. They shouldn't worry too much about punctuation at this stage.

MUM SAID…, page 26

Advise the children that you want them to look carefully at the pictures taken from the book and to write the appropriate sentence under each picture. As before, they shouldn't worry too much about the punctuation.

PLENARY

Share examples of the children's work. Encourage the children to read out their completed sentences. Ask those who completed 'Yes or no' why they chose *yes* or *no* in each case. Select children to identify the initial and final phonemes in the CVC words *mum*, *dad* and *yes* from their activity sheets.

EXTENSION

WORD BIRDS, page 27

Give this sheet to the children for homework. Explain that you want them to colour in the letters of the words and practise reading the words aloud to a parent or carer.

Yes or no

● Look at the birds. Do you think they are saying **yes** or **no**? Write in their speech bubbles.
● Complete each sentence. Then write out the whole sentence on the line.

My mum said, "_____."

_____

I said, "_____."

_____

Mum said...

● Look at each picture. Choose the right sentence from the bottom of the page and copy it out.

_____   _____

_____   _____

_____

My mum said, "Yes."

My dad said, "Yes."

I said, "No."

Word birds

● Colour the words. Read the words aloud.

Mum's birthday

HIGH-FREQUENCY WORDS: *THEY, ARE, GOING, TO, GET, (MUM)*

OBJECTIVES

Word level: to read on sight a range of familiar words, for example labels; to recognise the critical features of words, for example length.

Sentence level: to understand that words are ordered left to right and need to be read that way to make sense.

Text level: to track the text in the right order, page by page, left to right, top to bottom, pointing while reading/telling a story and making one-to-one correspondences between written and spoken words; to write labels or captions for pictures and drawings.

WHOLE CLASS TEACHING

Practise the new high-frequency words for this minibook, using the flashcards.

Whilst reading the book together, remind the children to track the text in the right order. Encourage them to finger-point while they are reading.

Emphasise that the words in are text are ordered from left to right and must be read this way to make sense. Demonstrate the importance of this by writing the words from page 4 in reverse order on a board or flip chart. Ask the children to help you read the 'sentence'. They should appreciate that it no longer makes sense. Write the sentence correctly and read it together.

Talk about the story in the minibook. Have the children ever helped to prepare a special meal or baked a cake for Mum or Dad? Encourage them to share their experiences. Can they recall the items that were bought?

Point out the labelled items in the illustrations.

GROUP/INDIVIDUAL WORK

WORD MAKER, page 29

Show the photocopiable sheet to the children. Point out that they should cut out the tiles at the bottom of the page and use them to spell each word. Advise them to look carefully at the lengths of the words.

SHOPPING, page 30

Explain what the children need to do for this activity, and make sure that they can read the labels in each of the pictures. Go through the example sentence to demonstrate how to write sentences to describe the action in the illustrations.

PLENARY

Choose two or three children from each activity to share their work. Encourage the children to check that each word in the word maker has the correct letters in it. For 'Shopping', ask the children to read their sentences aloud. Encourage this group to demonstrate finger-pointing when reading out their sentences.

EXTENSION

WORD PUZZLE, page 31

Go over the task with the children to make sure they know how to complete the puzzle – by reading the words, checking the number of letters and seeing where the letters will fit together. Point out that two letters have been provided to start them off.

Word maker

● Read the words below. Cut out the letters from the bottom of the page and stick them in the boxes to make the words.

they

are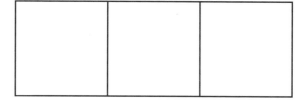

going

to

get

h	t	y	r	o	n	a	e	e
t	e	g	i	g	g	t	o	

Shopping

● Look carefully at these pictures and read the labels. Read the example, then write a sentence for each of the other pictures.

flour

They are going to get some flour.

eggs

_____

sugar

_____

Word puzzle

● Fit the words into the puzzle.

to   going   they
      are   get

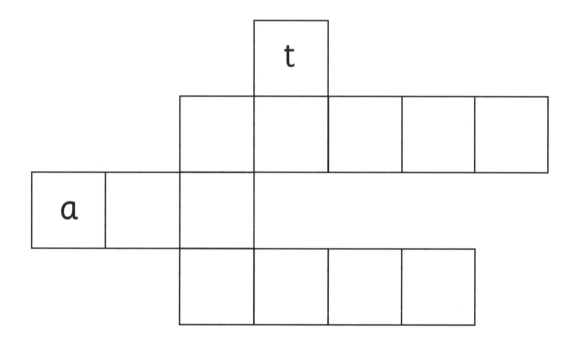

This is the dog...

HIGH-FREQUENCY WORDS: *DOG, WAS, IN, CAT, (THE)*

OBJECTIVES

Word level: to recognise the critical features of words, for example shape and length.

Sentence level: to understand that words are ordered left to right and need to be read that way to make sense.

Text level: to use knowledge of familiar texts to re-enact or retell to others, recounting the main points in correct sequence.

WHOLE CLASS TEACHING

Use the flashcards to introduce the new high-frequency words. Focus in particular on the word *was*. Point out to the children that whereas the other high-frequency words they are learning in this minibook can be 'sounded out' phonetically, *was* cannot be. Encourage the children to scan each page to find the word *was*.

Read the minibook together, reminding the children how they should track the text from left to right.

Encourage the children to retell the story in their own words, making sure they get the events in sequence.

Write two or three of the words from the minibook on a board or flip chart. Show the children that each word has a particular shape. Draw around the words on the board, indicating particularly the differences in letter height, and carefully erase the letters inside to leave just the shape. Extend this by drawing the shapes of some of the children's names on the board and asking them to try to work out whose names they might be. (You will probably need to give plenty of clues to help them work out the answers!)

GROUP/INDIVIDUAL WORK

SHIPSHAPE, page 33

Ask the children to find which word on the photocopiable sheet will fit which shape. Remind them to look carefully at the shape and length of each word.

PICTURE IT, page 34

Tell the children to read each sentence carefully and use what it says to draw what is missing from the picture. To ensure the children know what to do, read the first sentence together and establish what they should add to the picture.

PLENARY

Invite a few of the children to share their work. Check that the words fit precisely into each shape on photocopiable page 33. Let the children read the words aloud to the others. Ask the children who worked on the illustrations in 'Picture it', to read out the sentences and show their completed drawings. Invite the others to check that the correct character has been included.

EXTENSION

ORANGE CAT, RED DOG, page 35

Go through the instructions with the children, ensuring that they can identify the colours required for each word.

Shipshape

● Write each word into the shape it fits.

cat	dog	in	was	the

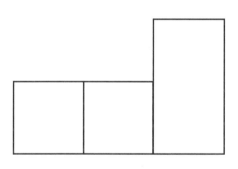

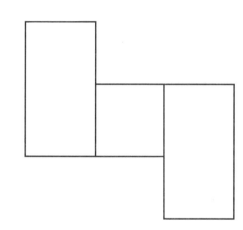

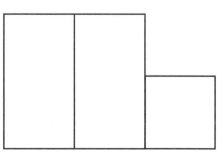

Picture it

- Read the sentences.
- Complete the pictures.

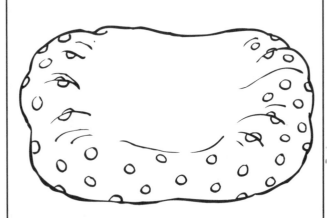

The cat was in the bed.

The dog was in the garden.

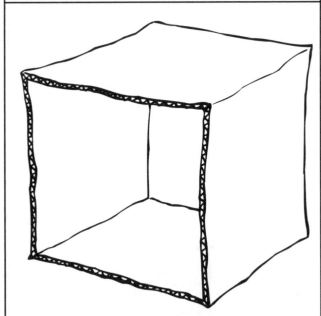

The dog was in the box.

The cat was in the tree.

Orange cat, red dog

● Read the words. Colour over the words in these colours:

cat – orange	dog – red	in – yellow	was – blue	the – green

cat   the   in   was

in   was   cat   in

the   the   cat   in

cat   the   was   was

dog   was   in   the

dog   in   was   the

was   dog   in   in

was   the   the   dog

Sunita's search

WHOLE CLASS TEACHING

Practise the new high-frequency words for this minibook using the flashcards. Revise the high-frequency words that reappear here – *she* and *the*. Remind the children of the *sh* and *th* sounds.

Read the minibook together. Encourage the children to track the text from left to right across the page and to finger-point as they read.

Ask the children to identify different parts of the book, for example *cover, title, beginning, end, page, line, word, letter*.

GROUP/INDIVIDUAL WORK

THE WORD AT THE TOP, page 37

Ask the children to look carefully at each of the words written above the illustrations. They should then cover the words and try to write them from memory three times on the lines provided. Remind the children that they should sound out the words in their heads, then write the letters that correspond to those sounds. Encourage them to proofread their work.

WATCH WHERE YOU WALK, page 38

Ask the children to find the letters for each word on the left and colour the paving slabs to spell the word. Stress that the letters are in order, but not necessarily next to each other, and that the children should track each word carefully to find it in the path.

PLENARY

Share the children's work. Encourage those who completed photocopiable page 37 to check that their spellings are correct and to establish where the errors are if they are not. Ask the children who worked on photocopiable page 38 to check that they have coloured the letters for each word correctly. Encourage the rest of the class to check for errors.

EXTENSION

JOIN THE WORDS, page 39

Ask the children to find all the matching high-frequency words on the sheet and link them with lines. Advise them to select a different coloured pencil for each set of words.

OBJECTIVES

Word level: to write each letter in response to each sound.

Sentence level: to understand that words are ordered left to right and need to be read that way to make sense.

Text level: to understand and use correctly terms about books and print: *book, cover, beginning, end, page, line, word, letter, title.*

The word at the top

● Look at the word. Cover the word, then write the word.
Try three times.

went

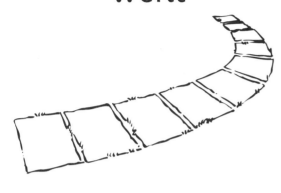

_____

_____

_____

she

_____

_____

_____

up

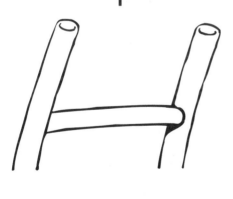

_____

_____

_____

the

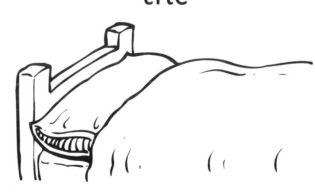

_____

_____

_____

● Check your spellings.

Watch where you walk

● Follow the path for each word. When you have found all the
letters in order, colour over them to spell the word.

went   n e t w v e m s n t

up   p n u s p a n p

she   e h s e h d e h

the   e t h s m a e

to   o m n t n o n

Join the words

● Join the matching words with lines. (One has been done for you.) Use a different colour to match each set of words.

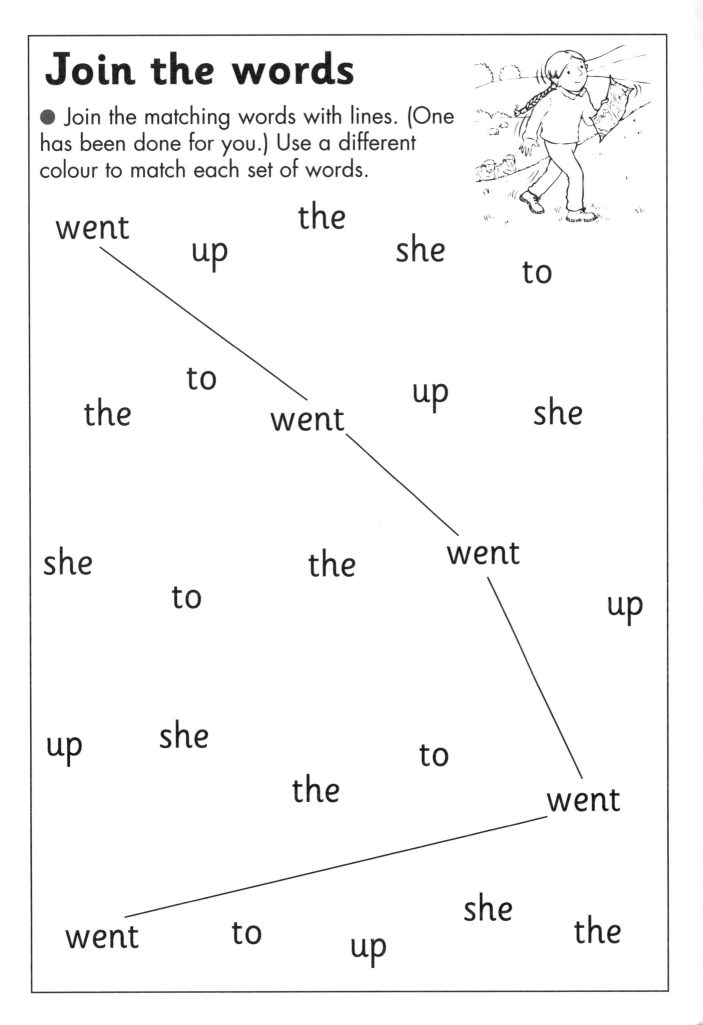

went   the   she
      up   to

the   to   went   up   she

she   the   went
    to   up

up   she   to
        the   went

went   to   up   she   the

Who goes there?

OBJECTIVES

Word level: to hear and identify initial sounds in words.

Sentence level: to expect written text to make sense and to check for sense if it does not.

Text level: to understand that writing remains constant, that is will always 'say' the same thing.

WHOLE CLASS TEACHING

Use the flashcards to practise the new high-frequency words for this minibook, prior to reading the text.

Read the minibook together. Point out that each sentence is asking a question and is punctuated at the end with a question mark rather than a full stop. Demonstrate how to read a question by raising the voice slightly at the end.

Encourage the children to predict the meanings of unfamiliar words by looking for picture clues and considering what words would make sense in those places in the text.

Tell the children to track the text to find the first instance of the word *big*. Write the word in large letters on a board or flip chart and ask the children to read it to you. Now write the same word in much smaller letters. Emphasise that it doesn't matter how we write the word, it still says the same thing.

Ask the children to identify the start sounds of some of the words in this book, for example **b**ig, **c**astle, **d**oor and **n**ose.

GROUP/INDIVIDUAL WORK

MONSTER STARTERS, page 41

Show the photocopiable sheet to the children and point out that they must look carefully at the start sound provided and then complete the word. Remind them to count the missing letters carefully to help them with this activity.

MONSTER'S WORDSEARCH, page 42

Explain to the children that they need to track the letters to find the words hidden in the puzzle. Tell them to circle a word each time they find one. Remind them of the work you did together in whole class teaching – that it doesn't matter in what format the words are written, they will still say the same thing.

PLENARY

Select children from each activity to show their completed sheets. Ask the children to read aloud the words they have made in 'Monster starters'. Ask the rest of the class to decide if they have chosen the correct words, bearing in mind the number of letters indicated for each word. For 'Monster's wordsearch', tell the children to check that they have circled all the letters required to make each word. Invite them to read out the words they found.

EXTENSION

HIDE AND SEEK, page 43

Ask the children to work on this sheet for homework. Explain that they should unscramble the words and write them correctly on the lines provided. They should then read the words to a parent or carer.

Monster starters

● Read the words in the box. Look at the start letter for each word below. Complete the word. Write the whole word again.

you	this	see	big	can

b_____   t_____

_____   _____

y____   c____

_____   _____

s____

_____

Monster's wordsearch

● Find the words from the box at the bottom of the page.
Circle the words in the door.

s	y	o	u	i
e	a	n	y	b
s	e	e	u	n
a	t	h	i	s
b	i	g	a	e
i	b	c	a	n

big	can	you	see	this

Hide and seek

● Sort each group of letters to make a word you know.
Write out the words.

A party

OBJECTIVES

Word level: to read on sight a range of familiar words, for example words from favourite books.

Sentence level: to understand that words are ordered left to right and need to be read that way to make sense.

Text level: to use experience of stories, poems and simple recounts as a basis for independent writing… through shared composition with adults.

WHOLE CLASS TEACHING

Practise the new high-frequency words in this minibook using the flashcards. Then read the text together.

Whilst reading, encourage the children to finger-point and to track the text across the page from left to right. Tell them to predict unfamiliar words by looking at picture clues.

Identify all the things the children in the book liked. Encourage the class to tell you what things they especially like.

Write the words *We like lots of…* on a board or flip chart. Invite the children to suggest endings for this sentence. Encourage them to help you spell their suggestions by identifying the initial sounds and end sounds in particular. Remind them that the words are strung from left to right across the board.

GROUP/INDIVIDUAL WORK

JELLY…, page 45

Using the flashcards, briefly revise the high-frequency words new to this minibook and check that the children can identify them easily. Go over the colour words listed on the photocopiable sheet, ensuring the children can identify them and use them to distinguish the words.

…AND ICE CREAM, page 46

Go through the instructions for this sheet, pointing out the wordbank at the top of the page. Explain to the children that they need to cut out the ice-cream halves from the bottom of the sheet and paste them to their matching halves above. They should then read and write the word made each time.

PLENARY

Share some of the children's work. Ask those who worked on photocopiable page 45 to check that the words have been coloured in correctly. Invite them to read the words aloud to the rest of the class. Encourage the children to read their words on photocopiable page 46 aloud to the others. Check that they have matched the ice creams correctly.

If necessary, give the children extra reading practice of these high-frequency words.

EXTENSION

BAGS OF SWEETS, page 47

Set this activity for homework. Explain to the children that you want them to cut out the word-sweets and paste them into the right bag. Encourage them to ask a parent or carer to listen to them reading the words aloud.

Jelly...

● Find the word in the jelly. Colour the word.

we – red
like – blue
of – green

...and ice cream

● Cut out the ice-cream halves from the bottom and paste them to the top ones to make words. Write the words on the lines.

of	like	we

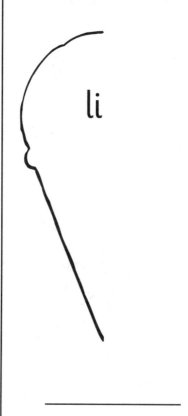

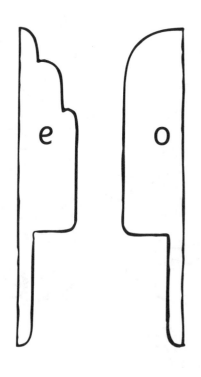

_____   _____   _____

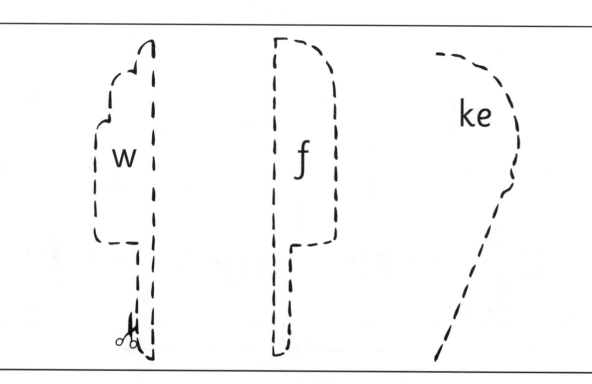

Bags of sweets

● Cut out the sweets and put them into the right bags.

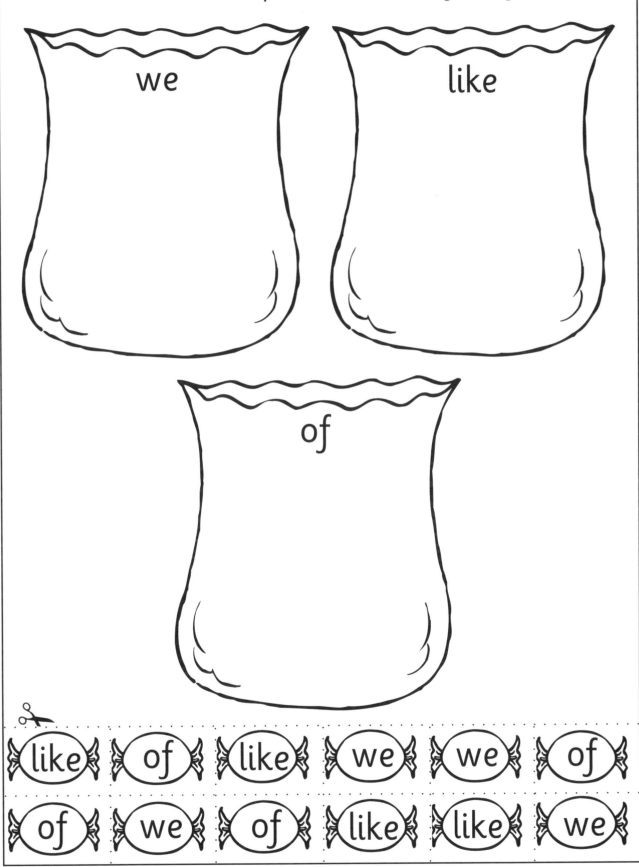

Coming and going

HIGH-FREQUENCY WORDS: *GO, AWAY, COME*

OBJECTIVES

Word level: to read on sight the words from texts of appropriate difficulty.

Sentence level: to use awareness of the grammar of a sentence to predict words during shared reading and when re-reading familiar stories.

Text level: through guided and independent writing, to write labels or captions for pictures and drawings.

WHOLE CLASS TEACHING

Practise the new high-frequency words for this minibook, using the flashcards, prior to reading.

Take the opportunity to recite some of the familiar nursery rhymes addressed in this book with the children. Talk about what happens in the story of each rhyme.

As you read together, encourage the children to predict difficult high-frequency words, bearing in mind what would fit sensibly in the context.

You could play the following game to reinforce these high-frequency words. Write the sentences *Go away* and *Come here* on two flashcards. Select children in the class to read and respond to the cards as quickly as they can.

GROUP/INDIVIDUAL WORK

CHARACTER LABELS, page 49

Explain to the children that they must trace each word label to the right nursery rhyme character. They should then copy the word on the line under the character. Remind the children to check their spellings as they write.

MISSING LETTERS, page 50

Explain to the children that they must find the missing letters to complete the words on the sheet. Advise them to use their minibooks and the wordbank at the top of the page.

PLENARY

Select children from each activity to show their work to the others. Ask the children from the first group to read out the words they have written on each character. Invite the others to decide if the words have been matched and spelled correctly. Ask the children from the second group to check that they have spelled their words correctly. Encourage the rest of the class to suggest corrections if they have not.

EXTENSION

HOW MANY?, page 51

Explain that the children must look carefully at the puzzle to see how many times they can find each word from the box. Suggest that they use a different colour to circle each different word as they find it. This will make it easier to tot up their totals at the end.

Character labels

● Find which word belongs to each person.
Then write the word underneath.

go	away	come

Missing letters

● Fill in the missing letters to complete the words. Then write out the words you have made.

go   away   come

a____y   _____

____me   _____

__o   _____

__om___   _____

__wa   _____

g__   _____

How many?

● In the puzzle, find and circle the words from the box.
Use a different colour for each new word.

go away come

a w a y g o a w a y c o m e

c o m e c o m e a w a y g o

g o g o c o m e a w a y g o

c o m e a w a y a w a y g o

I found

come _____ times, **away** _____ times

and **go** _____ times.

Surprise parcel

HIGH-FREQUENCY WORDS: *IS, IT, FOR, (YOU), (NO), (MUM), (ME), (YES), (THE), (DOG).*

OBJECTIVES

Word level: to recognise the critical features of words, for example shape and length.

Sentence level: to use a capital letter for the start of own name.

Text level: through guided and independent writing, to write their own names and to write labels or captions for pictures and drawings.

WHOLE CLASS TEACHING

Use the flashcards to practise the new high-frequency words for this minibook. Revisit all the revision words (shown in brackets above), and ensure that the children can read these words on sight.

Read the minibook together. Stop before page 8 and ask the children to speculate what might be in the parcel.

Talk about getting parcels through the post. Ask the children to recall any parcels that they have received in this way. How did they feel? Were the parcels for a special occasion? What was in them?

Examine some of the words from the book with the children. Encourage them to pay particular attention to the words' shapes and lengths. Point out that some words have exactly the same shape and length, for example *yes* and *you*. Remind the children that in these cases we must look especially carefully at the individual letters to work out what the words say.

GROUP/INDIVIDUAL WORK

WHO IS IT FOR?, page 53

Go through the photocopiable sheet together. Explain to the children that they should label each parcel, having decided from its shape who the likely recipient is. Point out the label for the parcel at the bottom of the page, and ask them to write their own names on this. Remind the children to begin their names with capital letters.

MAKE IT FIT, page 54

Ask the children to write each word in the box into its correct shape. Remind them to look also at the number of letters in the words. Point out that some shapes are identical and two or three words will fit them.

PLENARY

Share some of the children's work. Ask the children to read out the labels they have written for photocopiable page 53. Encourage the rest of the class to identify any errors. Tell the children to point out the capital letters at the start of their names and invite them to say what they think might be in this parcel, giving reasons for their thoughts. Together, check that each word has been written in the correct shape on photocopiable page 54. Ask the children to identify words with the same shape. How many words did they find that were the same length?

Take the opportunity to secure all the high-frequency words appearing in this minibook by revising them with the flashcards.

EXTENSION

HOW LONG IS IT?, page 55

Explain to the children that they need to look carefully at the words in the box to count the number of letters and then sort the words into the right parcels.

Who is it for?

● Who is each present for? Write the names on the labels.

 baby  Mum  dog  Sam

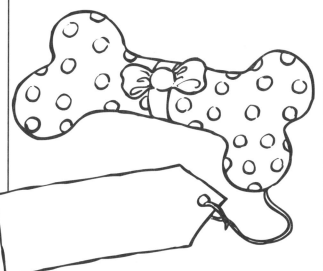

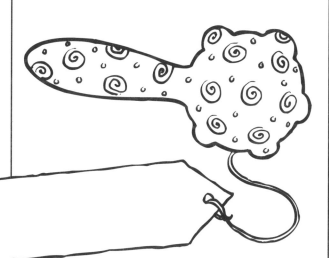

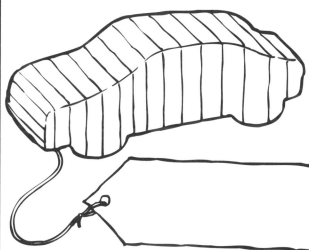

● This parcel is for you! Write your name on the label.

Make it fit

● Write each word in its right shape.

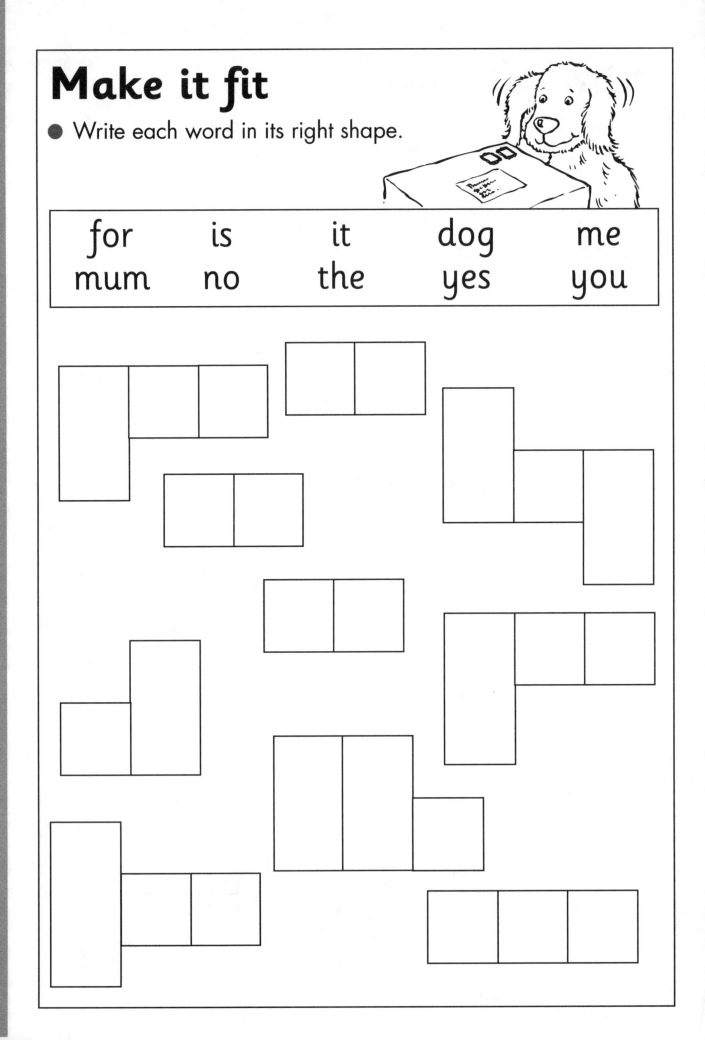

for	is	it	dog	me
mum	no	the	yes	you

How long is it?

● Look at the words in the box. Think about how many letters they are made of.

for	is	it	me	mum
no	the	yes	you	dog

● Sort the words into these groups:

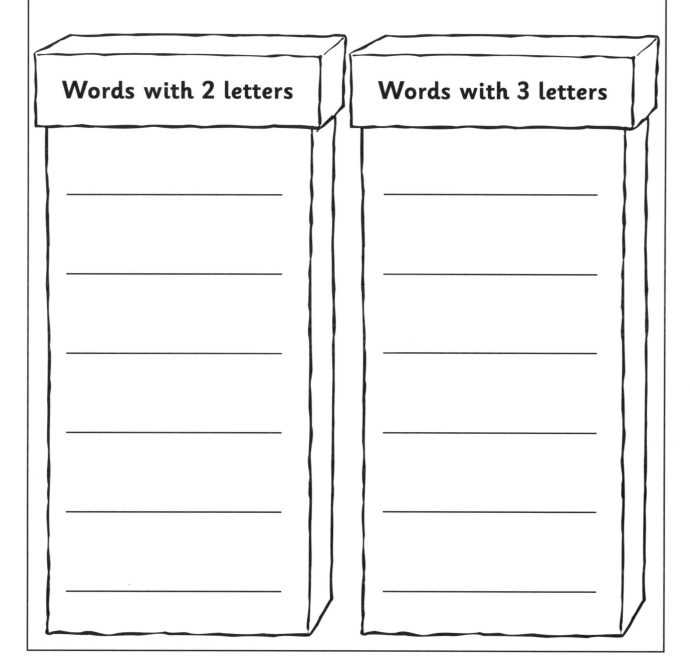

Words with 2 letters

Words with 3 letters

Record chart (1)

Use this sheet to record the child's reading and spelling attainment of the high-frequency words covered in the first six minibooks. Place ticks in the *Read* and *Spell* columns when the child has read and spelled the word correctly and independently.

Name: _____ Date: _____

WORD	READ	SPELL	WORD	READ	SPELL
a			look		
all			me		
am			mum		
and			my		
are			no		
at			on		
can			play		
dad			said		
day			she		
get			the		
going			they		
he			to		
I			yes		
			Totals	/26	/26

Record chart (2)

Use this chart to record the child's reading and spelling attainment of the high-frequency words covered in the second six minibooks. Place ticks in the *Read* and *Spell* columns when the child has read and spelled the word correctly and independently.

Name: _____ Date: _____

WORD	READ	SPELL	WORD	READ	SPELL
away			like		
big			of		
cat			see		
come			this		
dog			up		
for			was		
go			we		
in			went		
is			you		
it					
			Totals	/19	/19

I am a boy...

I am a boy.

1

I am a clown.

2

I am a pirate.

I am a lion.

I am a king.

5

I am a magician.

6

I am a firefighter.

7

I am a policeman.

8

The third little pig

Look at me!

Look at me waving.

2

Look at me laughing.

3

Look at me hiding.

4

Look at me huffing and huffing.

5

Look at me puffing and puffing.

6

Look at me running and running.

7

Look at me laughing!

8

Poor

Cinderella

I wash all day.

I sleep all day.

1

2

I cook all day.

3

I eat all day.

4

I sweep all day.

5

I shout all day.

6

I dance all day.

I search all day.

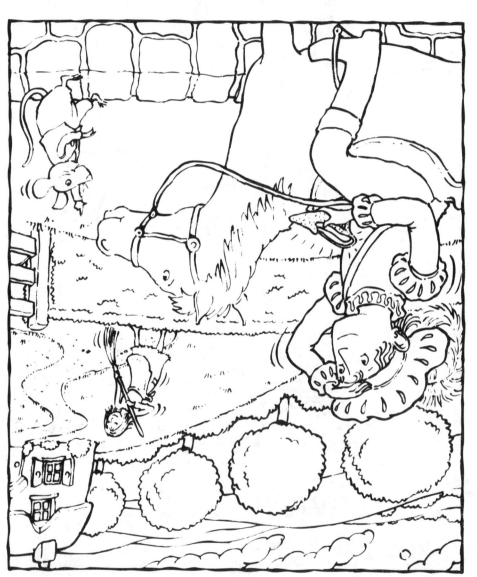

Playtime

He can play the
trumpet on a swing.

She can play the
drums on a bed.

1

2

He can play the triangle on a roundabout.

She can play games on the computer.

3

4

SCHOLASTIC TEACHER BOOKSHOP
HIGH-FREQUENCY WORDS

He can play football on the beach.

She can play hockey on ice.

He can play the
violin on a chair.

7

She can play
tricks on me!

8

Let's fly

My mum said, "Yes."

1

My sister said, "No."

2

My dad said, "Yes."

5

My sister and I said, "No!"

6

My sister and I said, "Yes!"

My mum said, "Yes."

Mum's birthday

1

They are going to
get some flour.

2

They are going to
get some eggs.

They are going to
get some sugar.

3

They are going to
get some cherries.

4

They are going to
get some candles.

5

They are going to
get some chocolates.

6

They are going to
get some flowers.

7

They are going to
get Mum.

8

This is the

dog...

The dog was in the garden.

1

The cat was in the house.

2

The dog was in the shed.

3

The cat was in the bed.

4

The dog was in the box.

5

The cat was in the
flowerbed.

6

The dog was in the
flowerbed!

7

The cat was in the tree!

8

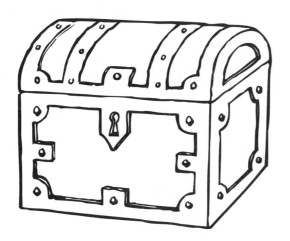

Sunita's search

SCHOLASTIC

Sunita went up the path.

1

She went up the road.

2

She went up the hill.

3

She went up the steps.

4

She went to the box.

She went up the ladder.

Sunita went home.

7

She went up to bed.

8

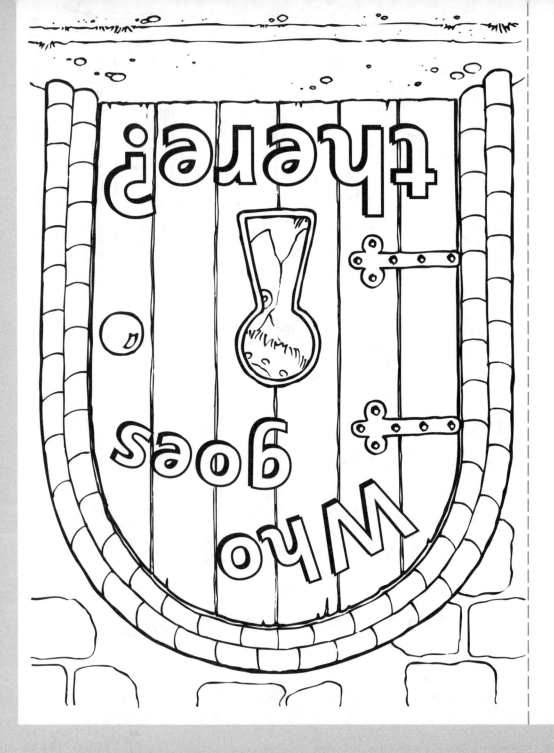

Who goes there?

Can you see this **big** castle?

Can you see this **big** door?

1

2

Can you see this **big** bell?

Can you see this **big** shoe?

3

4

Can you see this **big** hand?

5

Can you see this **big** nose?

6

Can you see this **big** smile?

Can you see this **big** monster?

A party

We like all of our friends.

1

We like lots of games.

2

We like lots of balloons.

3

We like bowls of jelly.

4

SCHOLASTIC TEACHER BOOKSHOP
HIGH-FREQUENCY WORDS

SCHOLASTIC
PHOTOCOPIABLE

We like lots of ice cream.

We like bags of sweets.

We like lots of dancing.

7

We all like hugs.

8

Coming and going

Oooh, go away!

1

Come for dinner!

2

Come over here.

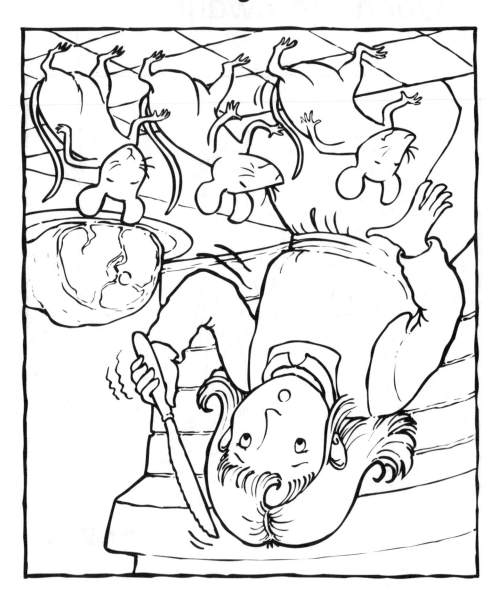

Go away.

Go away, rain.

5

Come back here!

6

Come back, Jack!

Please go away.

Surprise parcel

SCHOLASTIC TEACHER BOOKSHOP
HIGH-FREQUENCY WORDS

FLASHCARDS

I

a

my

no

in

of

me

it

up

he	at
on	we

is

go

am

to

SCHOLASTIC TEACHER BOOKSHOP
HIGH-FREQUENCY WORDS

for

and

you

are

cat

mum

dad

all

SCHOLASTIC TEACHER BOOKSHOP
HIGH-FREQUENCY WORDS

get

see

she

was

yes

can

day

big

look

like

the

dog

this	said
play	they

going

come

went

away

SCHOLASTIC PHOTOCOPIABLE

SCHOLASTIC TEACHER BOOKSHOP
HIGH-FREQUENCY WORDS